SUPER COOL FLIERS

Published by Top That! Publishing plc
Tide Mill Way, Woodbridge, Suffolk, IP12 1AP, UK
www.topthatpublishing.com

FOLDING TIPS

BEFORE YOU BEGIN ANY OF THE PROJECTS IN THIS BOOK, HERE ARE SOME HELPFUL TIPS THAT WILL MAKE YOUR FOLDING EASIER:

- *Before you start folding, make sure your paper is the correct shape.*
- *Fold on a flat surface, like a table or a book.*
- *Make your folds and cuts neat and accurate.*
- *Crease your folds into place by running your thumbnail along them.*
- *Carefully score along the marked lines using safety scissors and a ruler. This will make folding easier, especially as the lines become obscured towards the end of the model-making.*

SYMBOLS AND BASIC FOLDING PROCEDURES

These symbols show the direction in which paper should be folded. Although you won't need to use all the folds for the planes in this book, you can use them to create your own designs later.

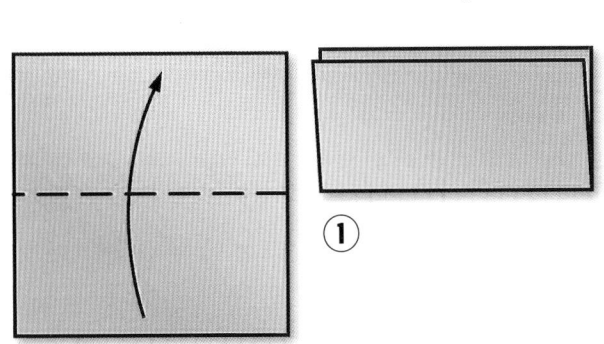

1. VALLEY FOLD (FOLD IN FRONT)

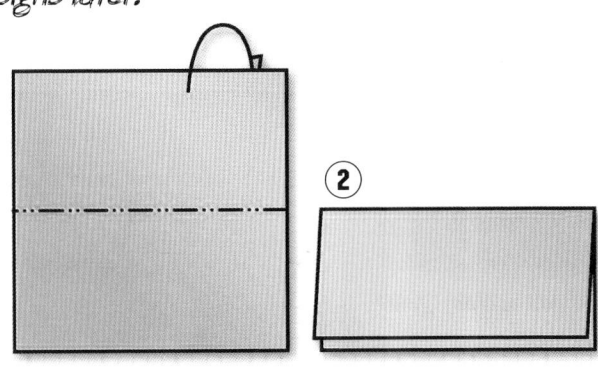

2. MOUNTAIN FOLD (FOLD BEHIND)

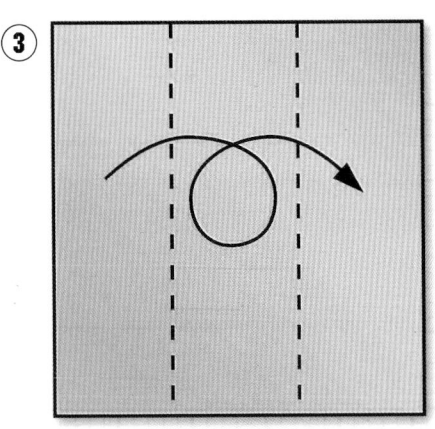

3. FOLD OVER AND OVER

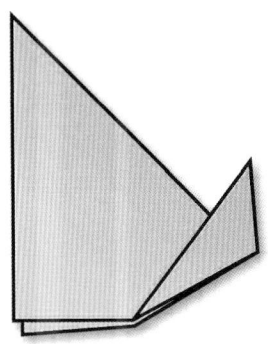

4. OUTSIDE REVERSE FOLD

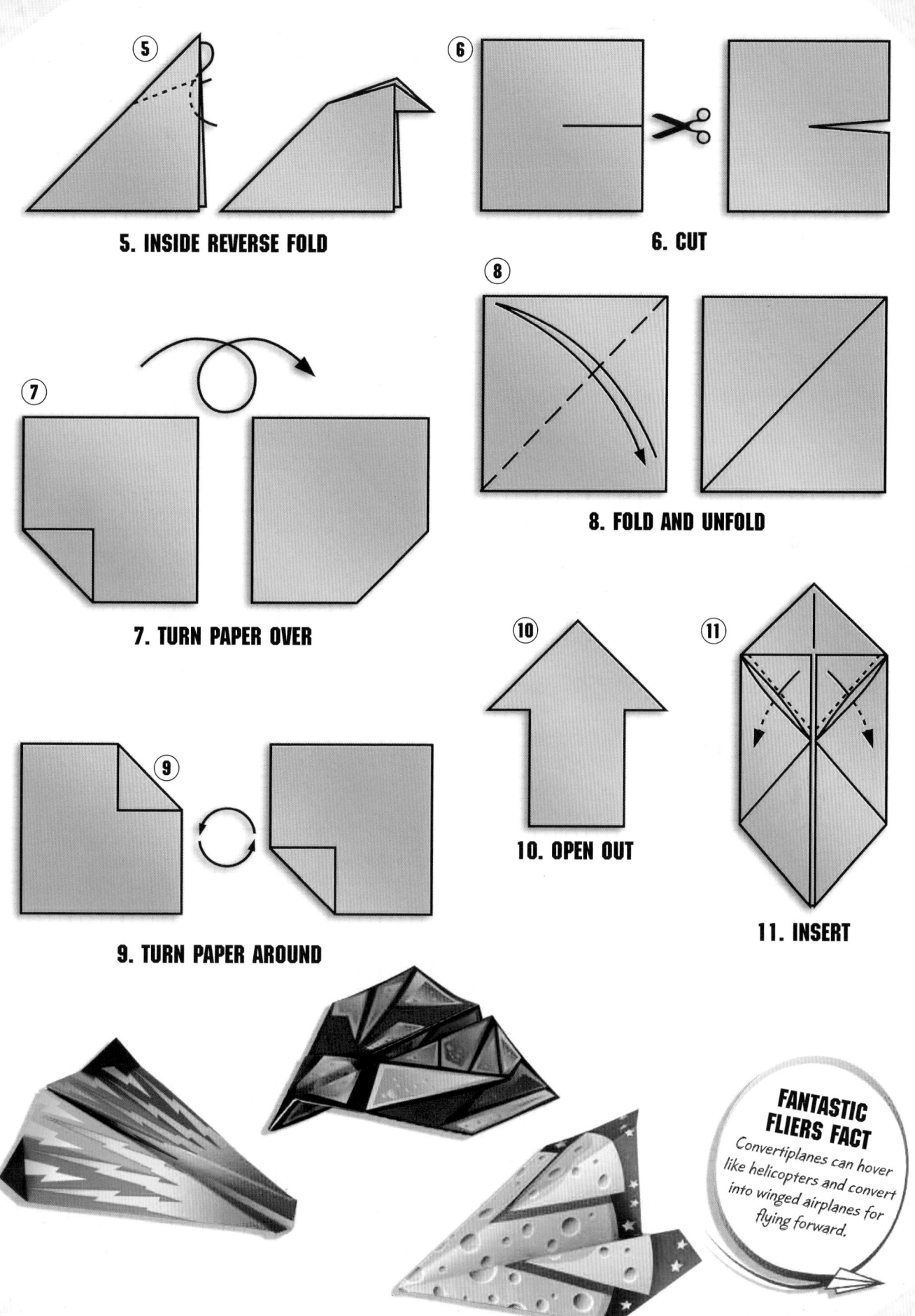

5. INSIDE REVERSE FOLD

6. CUT

7. TURN PAPER OVER

8. FOLD AND UNFOLD

9. TURN PAPER AROUND

10. OPEN OUT

11. INSERT

FANTASTIC FLIERS FACT
Convertiplanes can hover like helicopters and convert into winged airplanes for flying forward.

GROOVY JET

FOLLOW THESE FEW SIMPLE STEPS TO MAKE THE COOLEST JET AROUND.
USE THE PRINTED PAGE NUMBERED 1 AT THE BACK OF THIS BOOK.

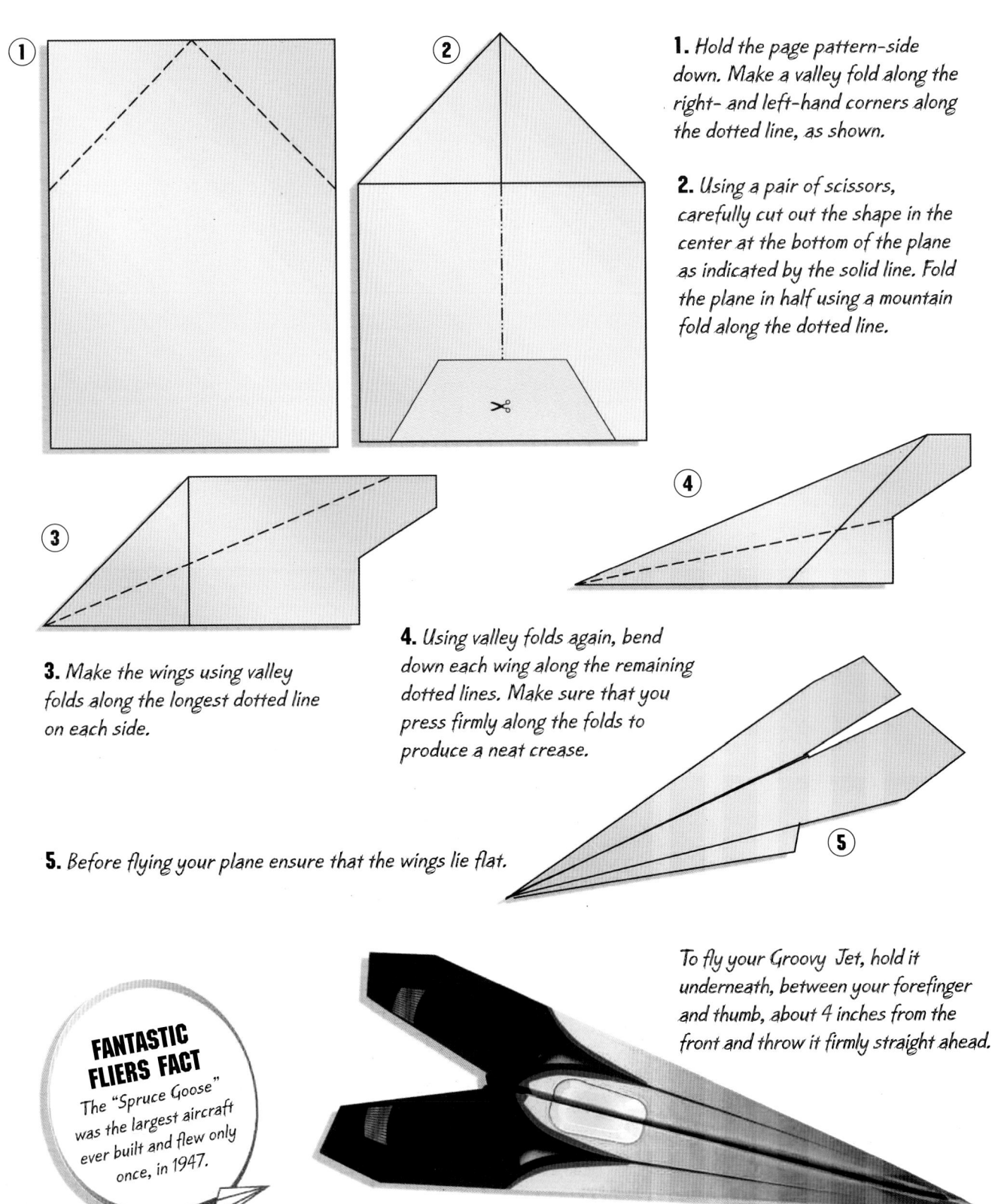

1. Hold the page pattern-side down. Make a valley fold along the right- and left-hand corners along the dotted line, as shown.

2. Using a pair of scissors, carefully cut out the shape in the center at the bottom of the plane as indicated by the solid line. Fold the plane in half using a mountain fold along the dotted line.

3. Make the wings using valley folds along the longest dotted line on each side.

4. Using valley folds again, bend down each wing along the remaining dotted lines. Make sure that you press firmly along the folds to produce a neat crease.

5. Before flying your plane ensure that the wings lie flat.

To fly your Groovy Jet, hold it underneath, between your forefinger and thumb, about 4 inches from the front and throw it firmly straight ahead.

FANTASTIC FLIERS FACT
The "Spruce Goose" was the largest aircraft ever built and flew only once, in 1947.

WHIZZING WEDGE

THIS PLANE WILL WHIZZ THROUGH THE AIR WITH THE GREATEST OF SPEED.
USE THE PRINTED PAGE NUMBERED 2 AT THE BACK OF THIS BOOK.

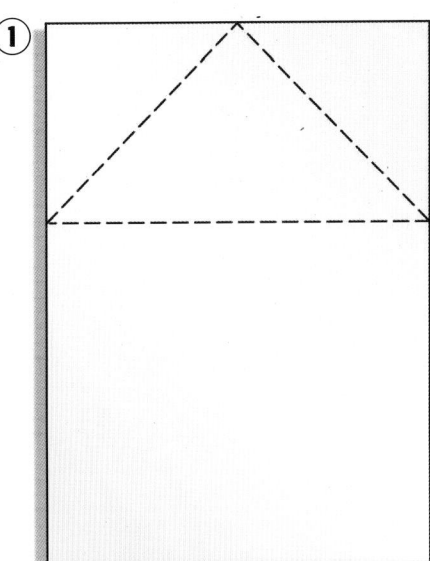

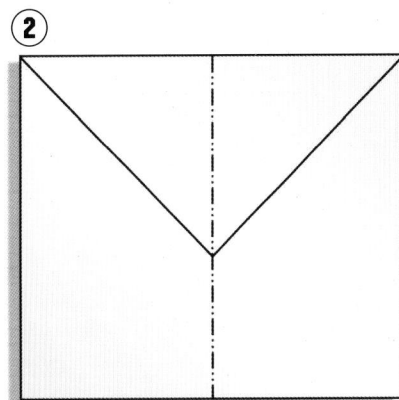

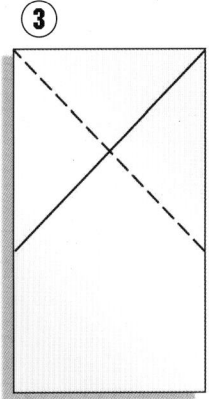

1. Hold the page pattern-side down. Make a valley fold along the right and left hand corners along the dotted line, as shown. Then take the triangle-shaped piece and bend it down in a valley fold, as shown.

2. Using a mountain fold, fold the whole plane in half.

3. Bend down both sides using the two shortest dotted lines you can see, using valley folds.

4. The wings are made by, again, making valley folds along the remaining visible dotted lines. Make sure that you press firmly to get neatly creased edges.

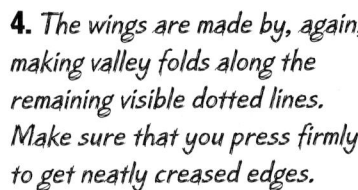

5. Before making a test flight, make sure the tops of both wings are flat.

To fly your Whizzing Wedge, hold it underneath, between your forefinger and thumb, about 3 inches from the front and throw it firmly straight ahead.

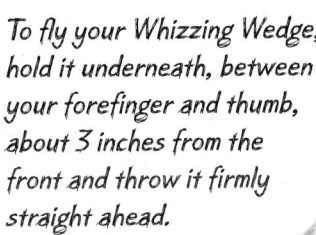

FANTASTIC FLIERS FACT
Chuck Yeager broke the sound barrier in the Bell X-1 in 1947.

GRACEFUL GLIDER

FOLLOW THESE EASY STEPS TO CREATE A GLIDER THAT WILL GENTLY GLIDE ALONG BEFORE COMING TO LAND. USE THE PRINTED PAGE NUMBERED 3 AT THE BACK OF THIS BOOK.

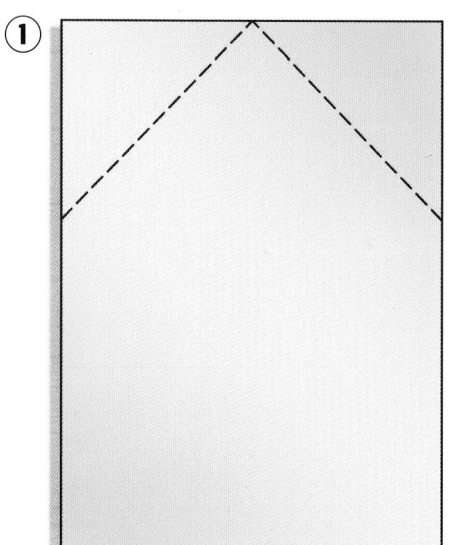

①

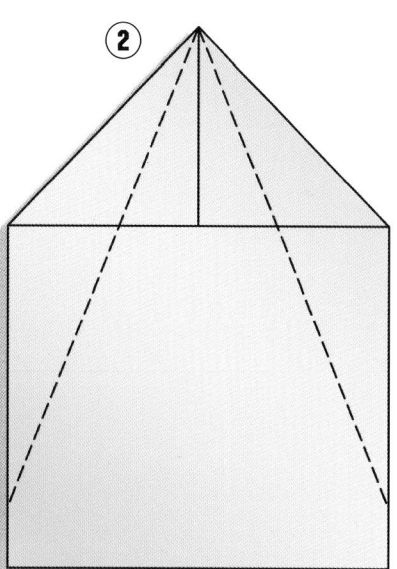

②

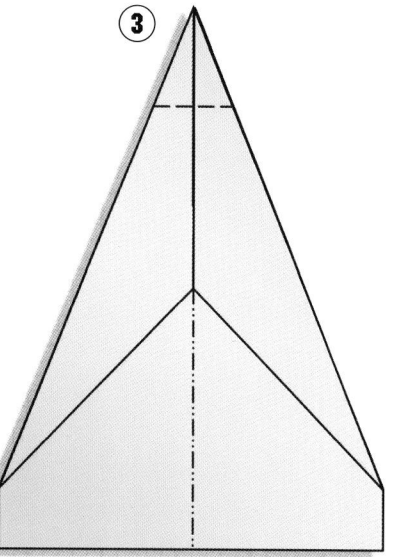

③

1. Hold the page pattern-side down. Make a valley fold along the right- and left-hand corners along the dotted lines, as shown.

2. Bring in the two sides by bending the dotted edges toward the center in valley folds, as shown.

4. Make the wings by forming valley folds on either side using the long dotted lines as your crease guide. Again, keep all your folds crisp and sharp by pressing firmly.

5. Bend up the corners of both wings using valley folds along the dotted lines.

6. Before flying your plane make sure the wings are angled slightly upward, as shown.

3. Take the pointed tip and pull it down toward you in a valley fold using the dotted line (at the level of the orange segments) for the crease. Fold the whole plane in half by bending a mountain fold along the center line. Keep your creases sharp.

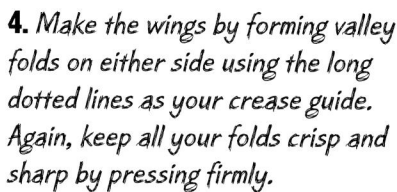

④

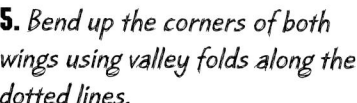

⑤

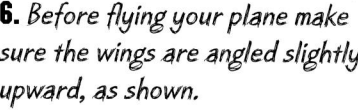

⑥

To fly your Graceful Glider, hold it between your forefinger and thumb, about 2 inches from the front. Your glider will perform a graceful glide before diving to the ground.

FANTASTIC FLIERS FACT
The stunt, Wing Walking, requires a person to move on an airplane's wing while in flight.

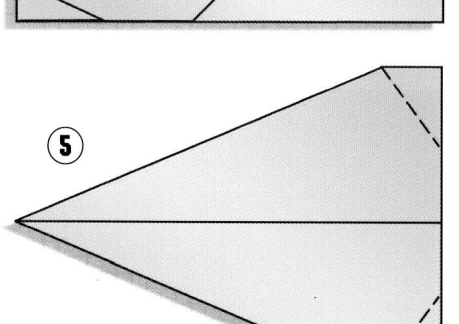

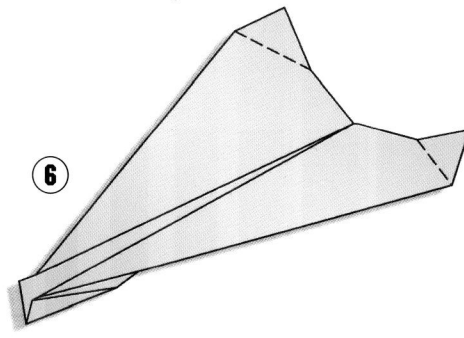

FUNKY FLIER

THIS WIDE-WINGED WONDER WILL ASTOUND YOU WITH ITS SPEED.
USE THE PRINTED PAGE NUMBERED 4 AT THE BACK OF THIS BOOK.

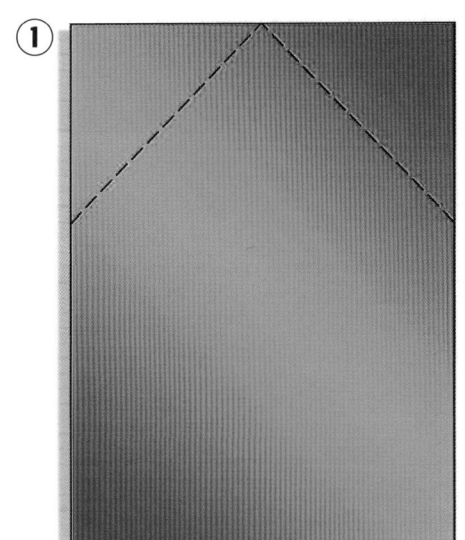

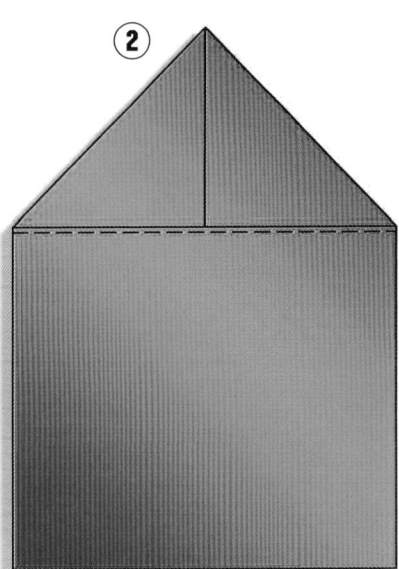

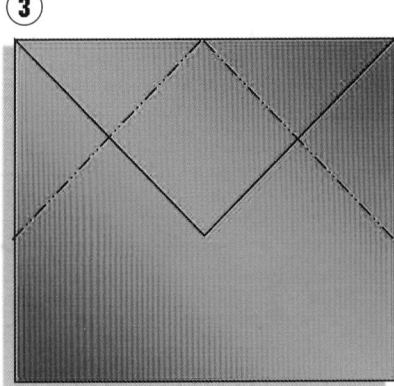

1. Hold the page pattern-side down. Make a valley fold along the right and left-hand corners along the dotted line, as shown.

2. Take the triangle-shaped piece and bend it down in a valley fold, as shown. Remember to use the dotted lines as the guide to where to fold.

3. Fold the top corners back in a mountain fold, along the dashed line, as shown.

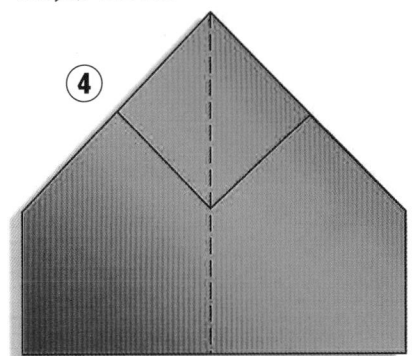

4. Fold the whole plane in half using a valley fold down the center dotted line. Press down firmly to make a neat crease.

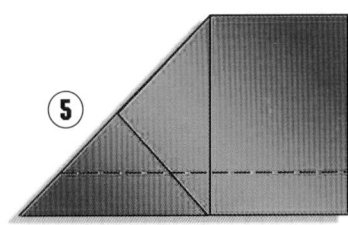

5. To form the wings, use valley folds on both sides of the plane. Use the dotted lines to guide your crease line.

6. Before you fly your plane, make sure the wings are completely flat.

Hold the plane underneath with your thumb and forefinger, about 3 inches from the front, and throw it gently forward.

FANTASTIC FLIERS FACT
The colored vapor produced by air display teams is made from dyed diesel vapor.

HIGH FLIER

MAKE THIS HIGH FLIER IN A FEW SIMPLE STEPS.
USE THE PRINTED PAGE NUMBERED 5 AT THE BACK OF THIS BOOK.

①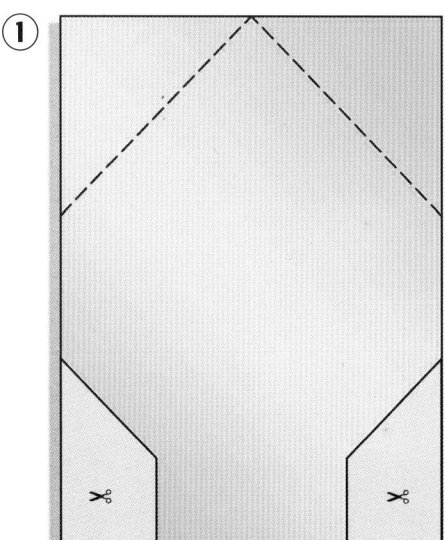

②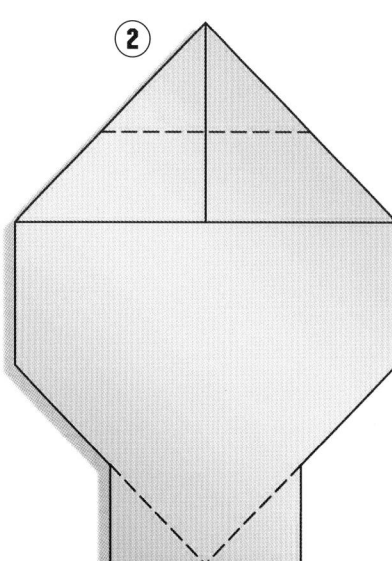

③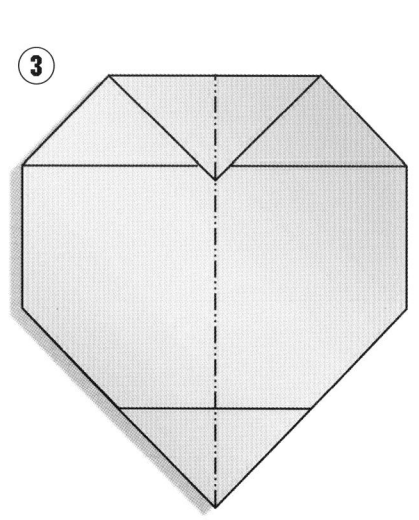

1. Hold the page pattern-side down. Make a valley fold along the top right- and left-hand corners along the dotted line, as shown. Using the solid lines as a guide, carefully use a pair of scissors to cut the bottom corners in the shape shown.

2. Take the top triangle-shaped flap and bend it down in a valley fold along the dotted line. Use valley folds to bend up the bottom corners into a V shape.

4. To form the nose, bend valley folds on either side of the plane using the dotted lines as your guide.

3. Fold the plane in half by doing a mountain fold along the central dashed line.

④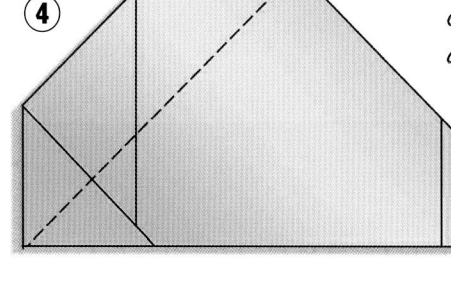

⑤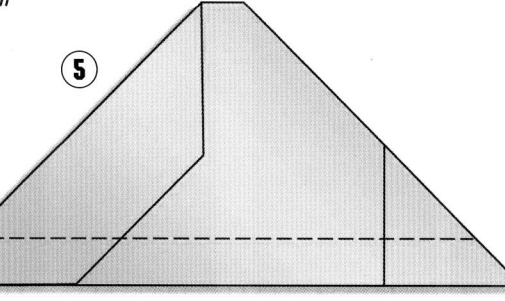

5. Form each wing by making valley folds on either side of the plane.

6. Before you fly your plane, bend the wings slightly upward.

To get your creation airborne, hold it between your forefinger and thumb about 2 inches from the front. Throw it hard and high.

FANTASTIC FLIERS FACT
The Gulfstream V is considered to be the world's first ultra-long-range business jet.

DAREDEVIL DART

THIS DARING DART FLIES HIGH AND FAST.
USE THE PRINTED PAGE NUMBERED 6 AT THE BACK OF THIS BOOK.

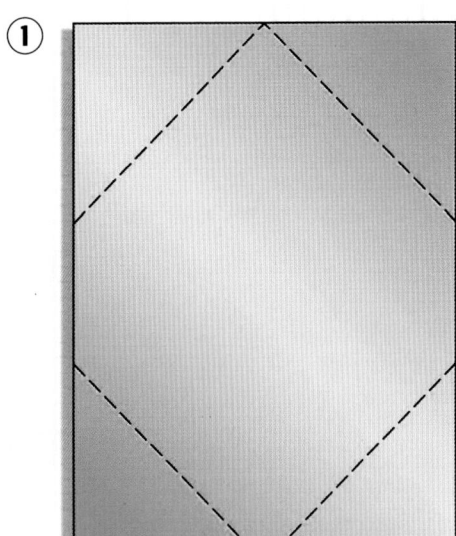

1. Use valley folds to bend in all four corners, as shown.

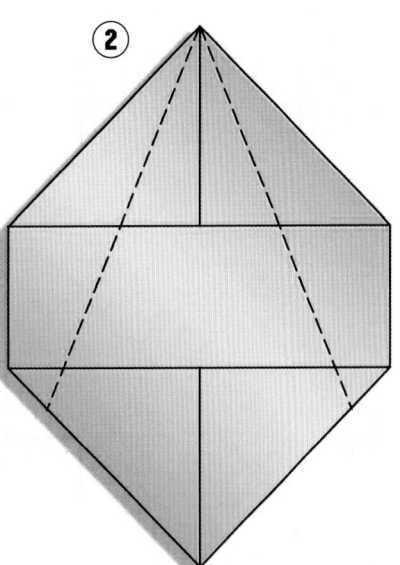

2. Bend in both sides at the top with valley folds, following the long dotted lines as a guide.

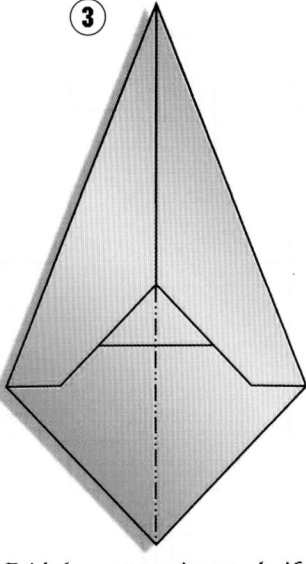

3. Fold the entire plane in half by using a mountain fold along the long dashed center line.

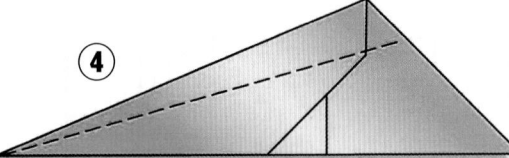

4. The first fold for the wings uses a long valley fold on each side, following the dotted lines.

5. The wings are completed by making a second valley fold on each side following the longer dotted lines.

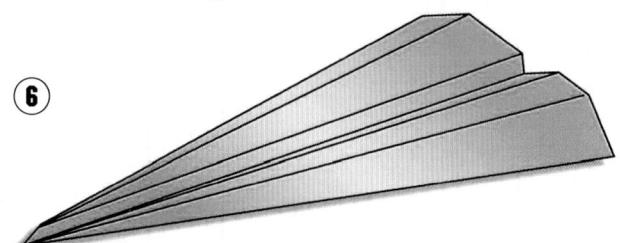

6. Before your flight, bend the outer edges of the wings slightly downward making an M shape.

To fly your Daredevil Dart, hold it underneath between your forefinger and thumb about 5 inches from the front. This plane flies best if thrown gently straight ahead at eye level.

FANTASTIC FLIERS FACT
As the MiG-25 blasts through the air, it gets very hot. Its skin is made from titanium metal which expands and flexes with the heat.

DELTA-WINGED DREAM

THIS DESIGN IS IDEAL FOR BEGINNERS—SIMPLE BUT VERY EFFECTIVE.
USE THE PRINTED PAGE NUMBERED 7 AT THE BACK OF THIS BOOK.

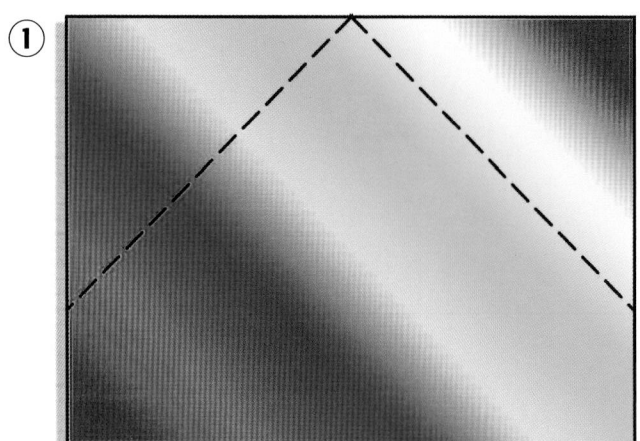

1. Hold the page pattern-side down. Using valley folds, fold the two top corners toward you along the dotted lines.

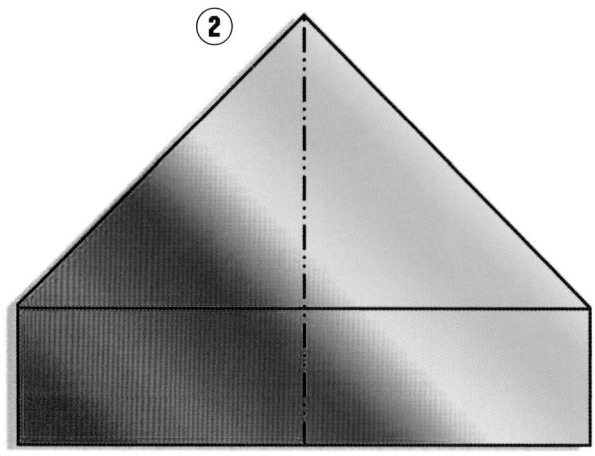

2. Firmly fold down the center of the plane along the dashed line, using a mountain fold.

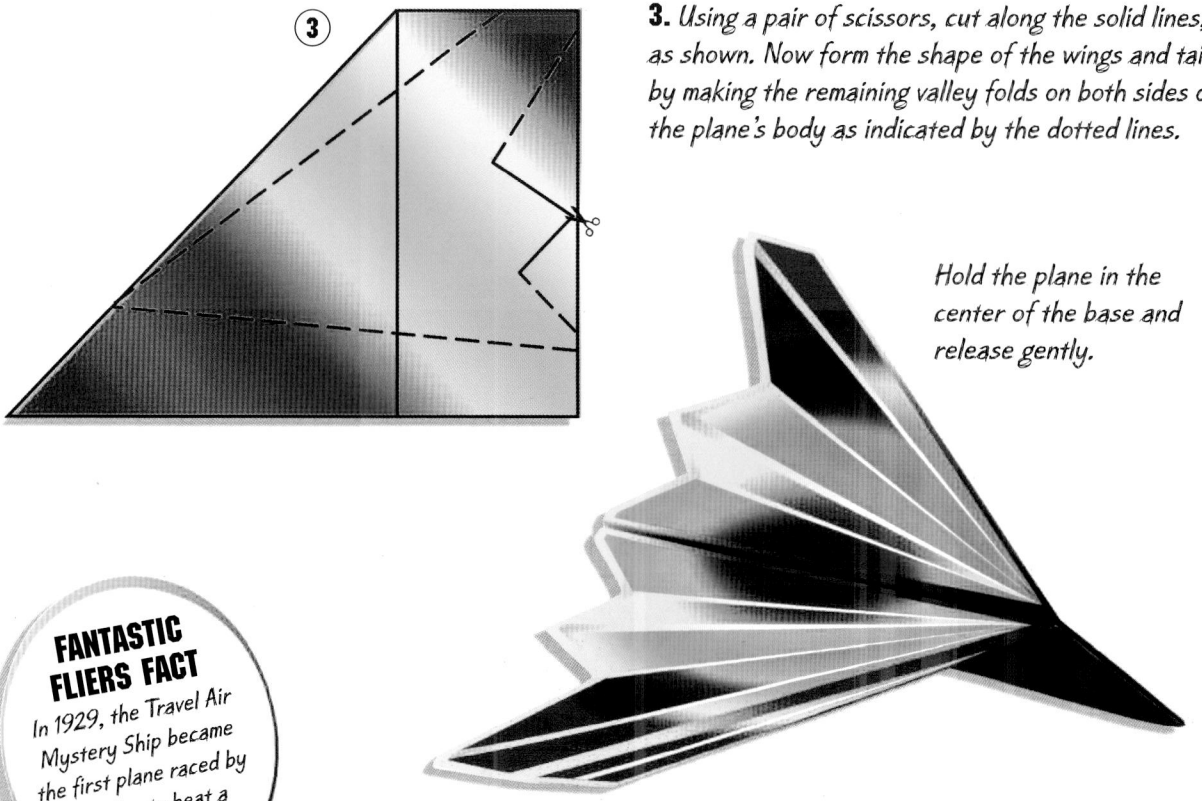

3. Using a pair of scissors, cut along the solid lines, as shown. Now form the shape of the wings and tail by making the remaining valley folds on both sides of the plane's body as indicated by the dotted lines.

Hold the plane in the center of the base and release gently.

FANTASTIC FLIERS FACT
In 1929, the Travel Air Mystery Ship became the first plane raced by a civilian to beat a military flier.

Problems flying your plane? Try weighting down the nose with a paper clip.

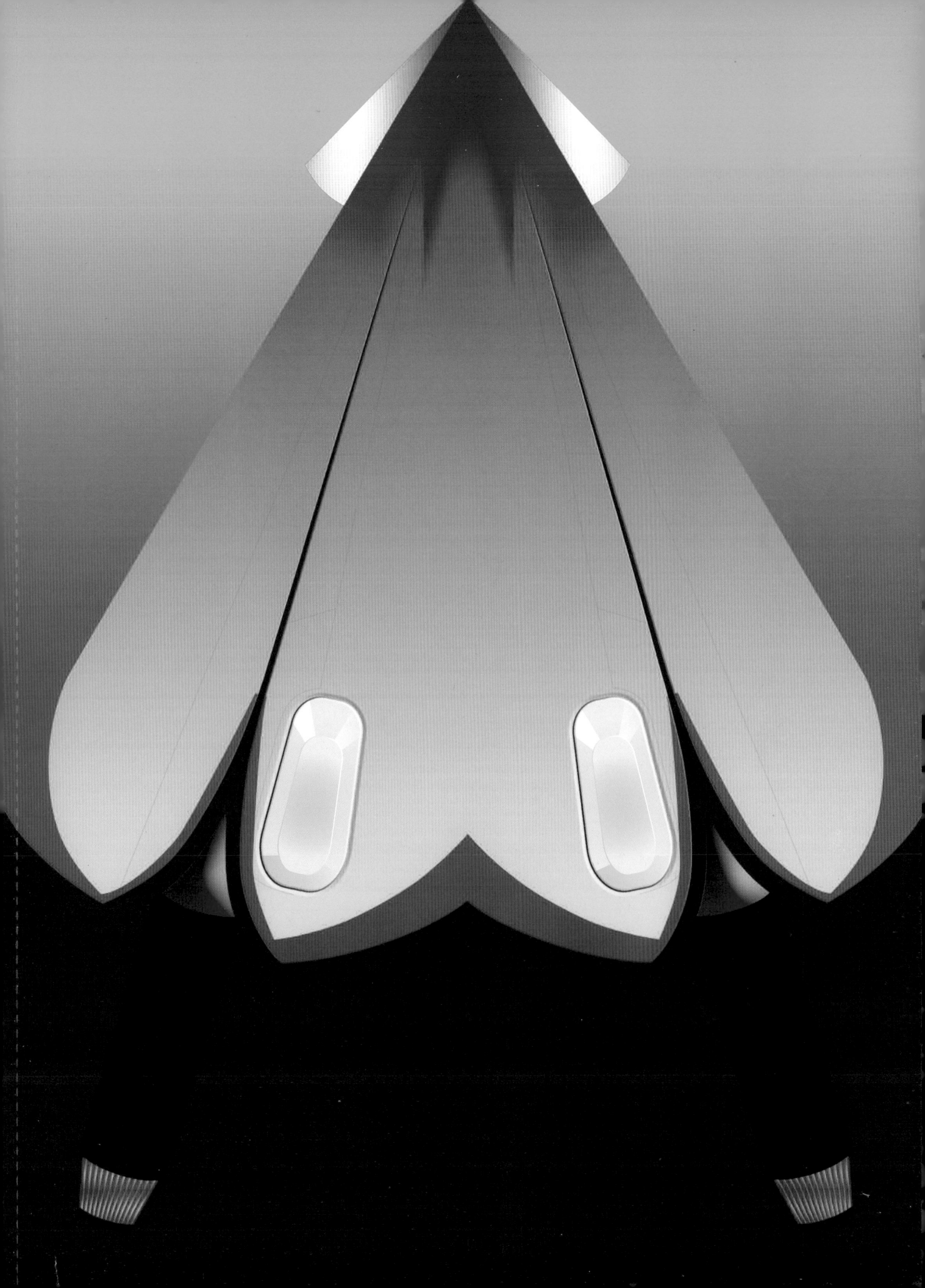

2

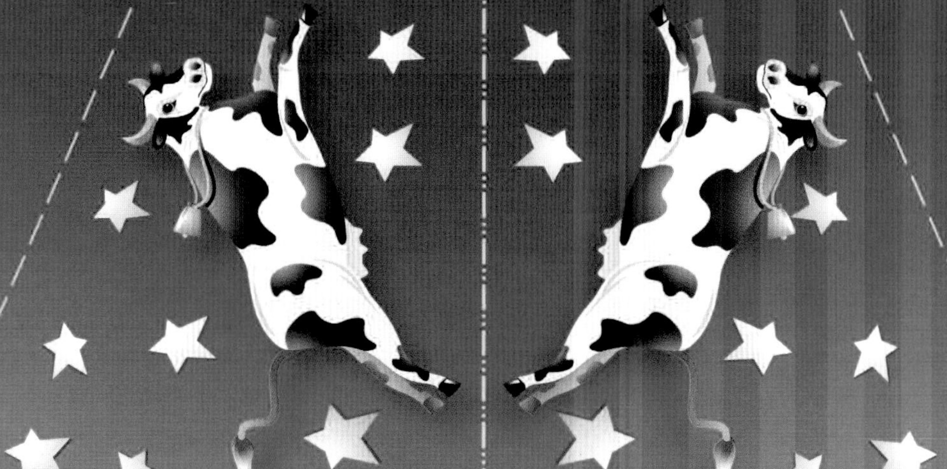

5

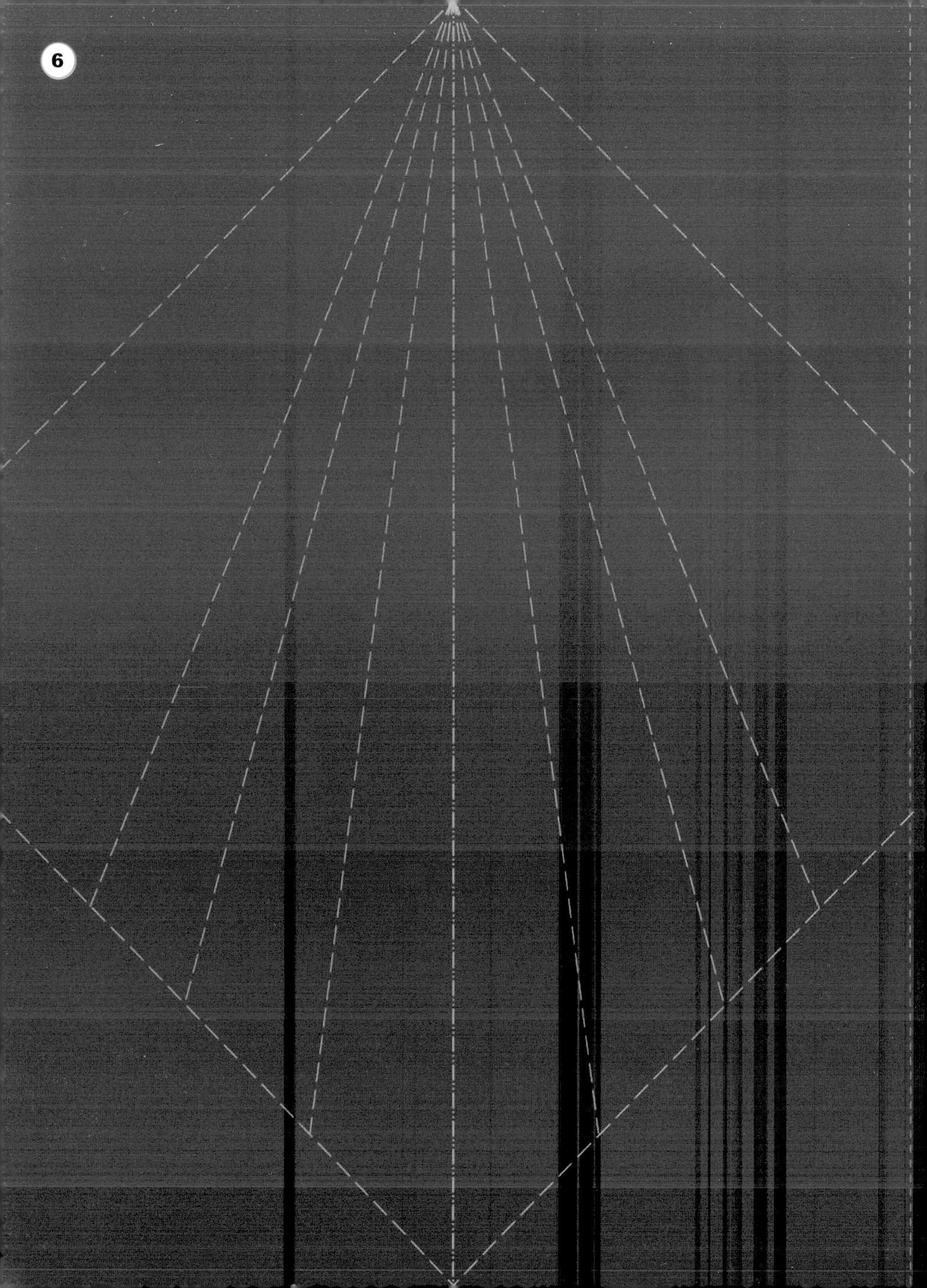